THE SILVER
COLORING BOOK

THE SILVER COLORING BOOK

ELEGANT SHIMMERING DESIGNS

ARCTURUS

ARCTURUS

© Arcturus Holdings Limited

ISBN 978-1-78599-791-4
CH005378NT

Manufactured in China

2   4   6   8   10 9   7   5   3   1

This sumptuous
coloring book based around the
theme of silver is decorated throughout
to celebrate the beauty of this precious
metal. Many of the images in these pages are
reminiscent of ancient arts, such as mosaics,
decorative tiling, and stained glass making. Each one
has a small amount of silver detailing already added
to give the picture a luxurious touch.
You can either shade the images in jewel colors
or in complementary metallic tones—just follow
your instinct and you will be amazed at the
results. So kick back, relax, and get
ready to enjoy a treasure trove of
coloring riches!

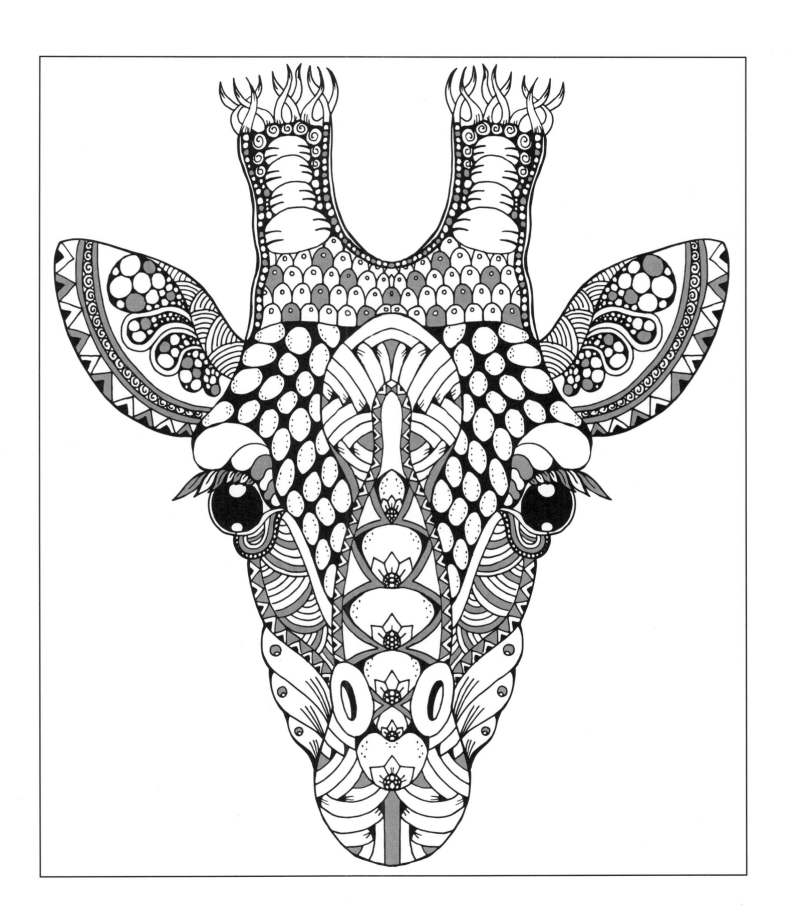

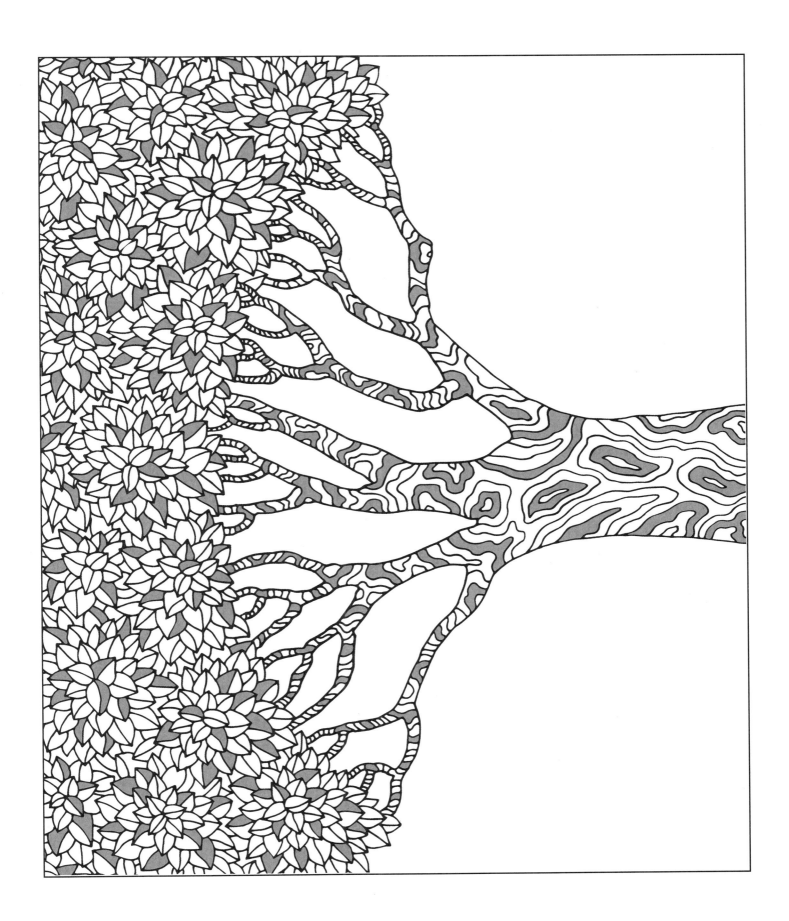